# James an Giant Peach

Roald Dahl

## STUDENT PACKET

**NOTE:**

The trade book edition of the novel used to prepare this guide is found in the Novel Units catalog and on the Novel Units website. Using other editions may have varied page references.

Please note: We have assigned Interest Levels based on our knowledge of the themes and ideas of the books included in the Novel Units sets, however, please assess the appropriateness of this novel or trade book for the age level and maturity of your students prior to reading with them. You know your students best!

SBN 978-1-56137-487-8

To order, contact your local school supply store, or:

Toll-Free Fax: 877.716.7272
Phone: 888.650.4224
3901 Union Blvd., Suite 155
St. Louis, MO 63115

sales@novelunits.com

novelunits.com

# Note to the Teacher

Selected activities, quizzes, and test questions in this Novel Units® Student Packet are labeled with the following reading/language arts skills for quick reference. These skills can be found above quiz/test questions or sections and in the activity headings.

**Basic Understanding:** The student will demonstrate a basic understanding of written texts. The student will:
- use a text's structure or other sources to locate and recall information (Locate Information)
- determine main idea and identify relevant facts and details (Main Idea and Details)
- use prior knowledge and experience to comprehend and bring meaning to a text (Prior Knowledge)
- summarize major ideas in a text (Summarize Major Ideas)

**Literary Elements:** The student will apply knowledge of literary elements to understand written texts. The student will:
- analyze characters from a story (Character Analysis)
- analyze conflict and problem resolution (Conflict/Resolution)
- recognize and interpret literary devices (flashback, foreshadowing, symbolism, simile, metaphor, etc.) (Literary Devices)
- consider characters' points of view (Point of View)
- recognize and analyze a story's setting (Setting)
- understand and explain themes in a text (Theme)

**Analyze Written Texts:** The student will use a variety of strategies to analyze written texts. The student will:
- identify the author's purpose (Author's Purpose)
- identify cause and effect relationships in a text (Cause/Effect)
- identify characteristics representative of a given genre (Genre)
- interpret information given in a text (Interpret Text)
- make and verify predictions with information from a text (Predictions)
- sequence events in chronological order (Sequencing)
- identify and use multiple text formats (Text Format)
- follow written directions and write directions for others to follow (Follow/Write Directions)

**Critical Thinking:** The student will apply critical-thinking skills to analyze written texts. The student will:
- write and complete analogies (Analogies)
- find similarities and differences throughout a text (Compare/Contrast)
- draw conclusions from information given (Drawing Conclusions)
- make and explain inferences (Inferences)
- respond to texts by making connections and observations (Making Connections)
- recognize and identify the mood of a text (Mood)
- recognize an author's style and how it affects a text (Style)
- support responses by referring to relevant aspects of a text (Support Responses)
- recognize and identify the author's tone (Tone)
- write to entertain, such as through humorous poetry or short stories (Write to Entertain)
- write to express ideas (Write to Express)
- write to inform (Write to Inform)
- write to persuade (Write to Persuade)
- demonstrate understanding by creating visual images based on text descriptions (Visualizing)
- practice math skills as they relate to a text (Math Skills)

Name_____

# What Do You Know About Insects?

**Directions:** After each of the following statements, write "True" or "False" in the "Before Reading" column. Compare your answers with a partner's. After you have read the book, label the statements again in the "After Reading" column. Circle the numbers of the answers that changed.

|  |  | **Before Reading** | **After Reading** |
|---|---|---|---|
| 1. | A centipede has 100 legs. | _____ | _____ |
| 2. | Farmers like ladybugs. | _____ | _____ |
| 3. | Centipedes are considered "pests"—harmful to crops. | _____ | _____ |
| 4. | You can tell a ladybug's age by counting its spots. | _____ | _____ |
| 5. | Centipedes are full of bones, like a fish. | _____ | _____ |
| 6. | A glow-worm is really a female butterfly. | _____ | _____ |
| 7. | A centipede has a sharp mouth. | _____ | _____ |
| 8. | Spiders are "pests." | _____ | _____ |
| 9. | A silkworm can really spin silk. | _____ | _____ |
| 10. | A grasshopper makes music by rubbing its feelers together. | _____ | _____ |
| 11. | A grasshopper's ears are on its tummy. | _____ | _____ |
| 12. | An earthworm's eyes are at the tip of its hind end. | _____ | _____ |
| 13. | Every grain of soil has passed through an earthworm's body sometime in the past few years. | _____ | _____ |

# Freewriting

**Directions:** Choose two or more of the following sentence-starts and freewrite for about ten minutes here or in your journal. (To freewrite, write without stopping to correct or change anything.  Just let your thoughts flow onto the paper.)

1.  In fairy tales, wicked stepmothers and witches … _____
_____
_____
_____
_____

2.  In fairy tales, little men with magic gifts … _____
_____
_____
_____
_____

3.  In fairy tales, lonely little boys..._____
_____
_____
_____
_____

4.  If I found a peach as big as a house..._____
_____
_____
_____
_____

5.  Talking animals..._____
_____
_____
_____
_____

# Study Questions

Write a brief answer to each study question as you read the book at home or in class. Use the questions for review before group discussions and before your final test.

## Chapters 1-6 (pages 1-15)

*Before reading Chapter 1, try to predict from the title and the picture on the cover what the story will be about.*

1. What happens to James Henry Trotter's parents?
2. How does James' life change after he loses his parents?
3. Where do Aunt Sponge and Aunt Spiker live?
4. How do Aunt Sponge and Aunt Spiker's names fit their appearances and personalities?
5. How do the two aunts get along with each other?
6. How do the two aunts get along with James?
7. Why is James unhappy?
8. What does the old man give James and why? Would you trust the old man if you were James? Does he trust the old man?
9. What is James supposed to do with the contents of the bag? What does he do instead?
10. What is shown in the picture on page 15? What happened right before what is shown? Does this remind you of any other stories, such as *Alice in Wonderland?*

    **Prediction:** What do you think the aunts will do about the peach?

## Chapters 7-12 (pages 16-31)

11. What different plans do the two aunts have for the peach?
12. Why do the aunts have a fence built around the peach?
13. How much do the aunts charge for a look at the peach? About how much is that in U.S. money?
14. How does James feel as he looks at the peach in the dark? (page 22) Do you think the author really understands what it is like to be a child?
15. Do you think James has ESP? How can you tell that he has "strange feelings" about what will happen?
16. How does James get into the peach? What does he find when he gets to the middle?

17. Do you think the insects have ESP?  How can you tell that they sometimes know what will happen before it happens?
18. How does James feel about the insects at first?  How do his feelings change?  Why?
19. Why does the Centipede call himself a "pest"?  If you were the author, what other "pests" might you add to the group?
20. Why does James like the centipede?

**Prediction:**  What will happen when the aunts discover that James is missing?

## Chapters 13-17 (pages 31-47)

21. Miss Spider and the others do some jobs that fit their abilities.  What are some examples?
22. Why does the Centipede ask James for help?  Why would most little boys consider this task somewhat of a nightmare?  What does James' response to the request tell you about him?
23. Why do you think the insects decide to move the peach?  How do they move it?
24. Who speaks in rhymes?  What other characters have you met in other stories who like to speak in rhymes?
25. How does the Centipede seem to feel about the adventure ahead?  Try writing your own poem about all the adventures you might have on your next trip.
26. What happens to the two aunts?  Do you think they get what they deserve?
27. Reread the beginning of Chapter 16, page 40.  What happens to the peach after it is released? Why do you think the author uses so many "ands"?  (Try reading that section out loud without the "ands."  Does it still show how fast the peach is rolling?)
28. The peach rolls over some famous towering white cliffs.  See if you can find out the name of these cliffs.
29. Where does the peach end up when it stops rolling?
30. How does everyone get to the top of the peach to take a look around?

**Prediction:**  How long do you think the peach will float on the ocean?

## Chapters 18-20 (pages 47-61)

31. How can you tell that the Grasshopper is an optimist and the Earthworm, a pessimist? Which are you more like?

32. James gets annoyed with the Earthworm for suggesting that they will starve. Why does he change his words from "Can't you see...?" to "Can't you realize...?" (page 49)

33. Why is the Earthworm against eating the peach? How does James convince him that it's okay?

34. What is the Centipede's song (pages 52-54) about? If you were to set it to music, what music would you choose?

35. Once the problem of food is solved, what new problem arises?

36. What plan does James come up with for escaping from the sharks? What else might he have tried? For instance, how might he have USED the sharks to get to shore?

37. Why are the insects all shouting out synonyms for "ridiculous" (page 59)? What other words might they have shouted out?

38. What does the Centipede mean when he says that the boy is "dotty" (page 59)? What is a more common word in this country for "dotty"?

39. Why does the Centipede predict that the Earthworm will be a martyr (page 60)?

40. What do you think James says when he reveals his plan (page 61)?

**Prediction:** Do you think the plan will work or will there be some "snags"?

## Chapters 21-24 (pages 61-74)

41. How does the Earthworm feel about being a decoy? Why do you think he agrees to do it?

42. How does James attach the silk to the seagulls? Can you think of another way he could have done it?

43. What is shown on page 67?

44. Why does Miss Spider climb down to the bottom of the peach?

45. Why didn't the sharks eat more of the peach?

46. A ship passes by. What route is it taking? (Trace the route on a map.)

47. How do the ship's officers react when they see the peach? What do you think would have happened if the peach had dropped near the ship, rather than disappearing into a cloud?

48. Who entertains the group? How?

49. Did you learn anything about grasshoppers from this chapter that you didn't know before?
50. Why does the Centipede tell James that he looks ridiculous (page 74)?
    **Prediction:** What will the travelers see as they journey through the sky?

## Chapters 25-27 (pages 74-88)

51. Why do farmers like earthworms?
52. Why do farmers sometimes bring in ladybugs?
53. Why was Miss Spider especially satisfied to see Aunt Sponge get flattened by the peach?
54. What are the Centipede's songs (pages 77 and 78) about?
55. How is each verse in the Centipede's song on page 78 like a limerick? Try writing your own limerick—about a wicked witch or stepmother in a fairy-tale who gets her "just desserts" in the end.
56. How does the Centipede get into trouble? (page 79)
57. How does James get him out of trouble?
58. What did the Grasshopper play when James went after the Centipede? Why? See if you can find out how this piece goes.
59. What do the travelers see as they pass through the clouds? How can you tell that these men are nasty?
60. How does the Centipede cause trouble with the Cloud-Men? Does he remind you of anyone you know—someone who stirs up trouble by not knowing when to stop joking around?
    **Prediction:** What do you think the Cloud-Men will do now?

## Chapters 28-34 (pages 89-106)

61. What is the arch the Cloud-Men are painting?
62. Why does the Earthworm say that he'd rather be on the end of a fishhook? Suppose each of the other creatures had told what they'd rather be. What might each have said?
63. How does the rainbow cause problems for those in the peach?
64. How do the travelers escape from the Cloud-Man who begins coming down the string? What do you think would have happened if the Cloud-Man had landed on the peach?
65. How do the Cloud-Men react when they see their fellow Cloud-Man carried out?

66. What new problem does the Centipede have?
67. Why does Miss Spider detest paint so much?
68. How are the travelers almost drowned? Why does the Centipede sing a happy song afterward?
69. The travelers catch more glimpses of the Cloud-Men. Which scenes stick in your memory?
70. How does James plan to get the peach to the ground? How is the plan ruined? Trace on a map the route the peach has come.

**Prediction:** How do you think people will react when they see the peach land?

## Chapters 35-39 (pages 106-119)

71. Why aren't the travelers killed in the crash? Where do they end up? As the author, where would you have had them land?
72. What is funny about the Chief of Police's saying, "Ahoy there! Come out and show yourselves"?
73. Do the New Yorkers welcome the strangers? How does their attitude confirm stereotypes about New Yorkers—or stereotypes of Americans often found in old science fiction movies when aliens show up? How can you tell that this story was written in the early 1960's? What effect was the Cold War having on Americans at that time?
74. People speculate about what kind of monsters these are. Which of the words (pages 109-110) refer to "real" monsters, and which are made-up words?
75. What is funny about the head of the Fire Department's exclamation, "Snakes and ladders!" (page 110)?
76. How do the New Yorkers change toward the travelers? Why?
77. What is unusual about the way James introduces the insects? Where do you think he learned this type of speech?
78. How do you think the travelers get down from the peach?
79. Who makes a speech of welcome? What do you think he says?
80. What happens to the peach? What happens to each of the characters? Why is it appropriate that the Ladybug marries the head of the Fire Department? If you were to rewrite the epilogue, how would you have had each insect end up?

Name_____

# Vocabulary

| | | | |
|---|---|---|---|
| paddle 1 | ramshackle 2 | desolate 3 | peculiar 4 |
| fantastically 4 | spectacles 5 | beckoning 8 | luminous 8 |
| centipedes 12 | hideous 13 | gracious 14 | |

**Directions:** Divide into small groups and map each of the list words together.

**Step 1:** Assign each person one part of each map. One person finds synonyms; the second finds or draws pictures; the third writes definitions; the fourth writes sentences.

**Step 2:** Turn to the pages on which the words appear in the book.

**Step 3:** Look at how each word is used.

**Step 4:** Complete maps for each word. (To do maps for all eleven words, you will need this activity page plus ten more pieces of paper.)

**Step 5:** Share your maps with other groups.

**Synonyms**
(words with the same meaning)

_____
_____
_____
_____

**Magazine Cut-out or Your sketch to Show What the Word Means:**

**Word:**

_____

**Definition in Your Words:** _____
_____
_____

**Word Used in a Sentence:**_____
_____
_____
_____
_____.

Name_____

| absolutely 16 | extraordinary 16 | mammoth 17 | inspecting 19 |
|---|---|---|---|
| massive 19 | marvel 20 | shilling 20 | seething 21 |
| bittersweet 25 | murky 25 | gigantic 25 | stone 25 |
| bolt 26 | reclining 26 | intently 26 | scarlet 26 |
| magnificent 26 | famished 27 | positively 27 | glassy 27 |
| disagreeable 28 | approval 29 | marvelous 29 | withering 29 |
| slither 29 | scornful 29 | colossal 30 | hysterics 31 |

**A. Step 1:** Form two teams of 3 or 4 people each and agree on how long the game will last. Cut out the words and put them face down on a table.

**Step 2:** A player from **Team A** picks one of the vocabulary words and makes a drawing while teammates try to guess the word.

**Step 3:** After three minutes, time is up. A person from **Team B** picks a word and draws it for his or her teammates.

*When game-time is up, the team with the greatest number of points wins.*

**B.** Each student writes the vocabulary word that matches each definition or synonym, below.

1. _____ miracle, wonder
2. _____ hungry, starved
3. _____ churning, agitating
4. _____ with an attitude of great concentration
5. _____ arrogant, contemptuous
6. _____ shriveling, wasting away
7. _____ pit in the middle of a fruit
8. _____, _____ four words from the list that mean "very large"
   _____, _____
9. _____ sweet and sour at the same time
10. _____ escape, flee

# Vocabulary

**Directions:** Do this activity with a partner.  One partner draws a <u>dotted</u> line around two words in each group that are <u>opposite</u> in meaning.   The other partner draws a <u>solid</u> line around the two words in each group that are <u>similar</u> in meaning.  Partners should help each other choose and discuss their answers.

1. chaos          paddock          hayride
   order          stable           trifle

2. bleak          repulsive        visible
   desolate       comely           venomous

3. panicked       knotted          staggered
   chorused       disentangled     lurched

4. vertically     insidiously      literally
   horizontally   treacherously    wretchedly

5. ignore         depart           amble
   gape           jostle           saunter

6. gossamer       sonorously       elementary
   cobweb         obviously        complicated

7. tumultuously   hurtling         stampeding
   serenely       rushing          jostling

Name_____

**Directions:** Form a group of three and figure out the mystery words together.
   Step <u>1:</u>    Each member of the group picks a card from the same set and reads the clue on it to the others in the group.
   Step <u>2:</u>    Members help each other figure out the mystery word for that set of clues. (Take a look at the vocabulary box only if you are stumped.)
   Step <u>3:</u>    Make clue cards for the other words in the vocabulary box. Play again.

## Cards in Set #1:

| Queen Elizabeth is more likely to use this word than Liz from Queens. | If you can read this, you're too big to ride in one but just the right size to push it. | This comes from a Latin word that means "walk around." |
|---|---|---|

## Cards in Set #2:

| This isn't a type of bear, but its homophone is. | horrible or gruesome | a murder or a monster might be this |
|---|---|---|

## Cards in Set #3:

| You could use one of this word's five syllables to make brownies. | wild uproar | Another word for "devil" is found in this word. |
|---|---|---|

## Cards in Set #4:

| This two-syllable word comes from the Old English "gaestan": to frighten. | If you were this, your mouth might well be hanging open. | This word rhymes with a synonym for "speedy." |
|---|---|---|

| | | | | |
|---|---|---|---|---|
| current | vast | babbling | disappointment | perish |
| grisly | starvation | affectionately | glorious | bluebottle |
| anxiously | cruising | perambulator | lunge | aghast |

Name_____

| | | | |
|---|---|---|---|
| boiling 61 | exhorting 62 | frantically 62 | tethered 64 |
| hovered 65 | delicately 65 | majestically 66 | ascent 67 |
| clambered 68 | funnels 69 | teeming 69 | spellbound 71 |
| inferior 72 | katydids 73 | rambunctious 74 | |

**Directions:** An <u>analogy</u> is a comparison.  For example:

**COLD** is to **HOT** as **GOOD** is to **BAD**.
(Both pairs are opposites.)

**SKUNK** is to **ANIMAL** as **IVY** is to **PLANT**.
(A skunk is a kind of animal.  Ivy is a kind of plant.)

Complete each of the following analogies with a word from the vocabulary list.

1.   ROBINS are to SPARROWS as GRASSHOPPERS are to _____.

2.   ROPE is to _____ as THREAD is to STITCHED.

3.   COLD is to HOT  as _____ is to BETTER.

4.   TAME is to DOCILE  as UNRULY is to _____.

5.   DOWN is to DESCENT as UP is to _____.

Write analogies for five of the remaining vocabulary words and give to a partner to solve.  (Leave the last line blank, but keep a list of your answers.)

6.   _____is to_____ as_____ is to _____.

7.   _____is to_____ as_____ is to _____.

8.   _____is to_____ as_____ is to _____.

9.   _____is to_____ as_____ is to _____.

10.  _____is to_____ as_____ is to _____.

# Acrostic

vital 75          modestly 75          saucy 76          teetering 79
frantically 79    companions 81        menacing 81       overwhelming 81
stealthy 82       wraithlike 82        lurking 83        imbeciles 85
loathsome 86      evidently 87         infuriated 87

Find the missing word for each clue. Write the letters of the word in the space above the numbers. Then transfer the numbered letters to the numbered spaces inside the worm at the bottom of the page. A message from the Earthworm will appear.

**Definition**                                                **Word**

1.  enraged, exasperated          __ __ __ __ __ __ __ __ __
                                     1  12  6              24

2.  essential, imperative         __ __ __ __ __
                                   10      2  8

3.  ominous, sinister             __ __ __ __ __ __ __
                                      11

4.  idiots, blockheads            __ __ __ __ __ __ __ __ __
                                     4  14 15 16    25 20  7

5.  ghostly, like an apparition   __ __ __ __ __ __ __ __ __
                                   21  3          23          22

6.  abhorrent, odious             __ __ __ __ __ __ __ __
                                    9  17 27    13       5

7.  skulking, prowling            __ __ __ __ __ __
                                   33 18

8.  accomplices, comrades         __ __ __ __ __ __ __ __ __
                                   31    26       32 31    30

9.  devastating, dominant         __ __ __ __ __ __ __ __ __ __ __
                                      29       28

10. brazen, cheeky                __ __ __ __ __
                                   19

__ __ __ __ __ __ __ __ __ __ __ __ __ __ __ __ __ __ __ __
1  2  3  4  5  6  7  8  9  10 11 12 13 14 15 16 17 18 19 20

__ __ __ __ __ __ __ __ __ __ __ __ __
21 22 23 24 25 26 27 28 29 30 31 32 33

*James and the Giant Peach*
Activity #9: **Vocabulary**
Chapters 28-35
**Note:** This activity has two pages.

Name_____

# Vocabulary

| | | | | |
|---|---|---|---|---|
| arch 89 | hypnotized 90 | enthralled 91 | malevolently 92 | kipper 93 |
| flabbergasted 93 | encased 95 | detest 95 | permanently 95 | proposal 96 |
| considered 96 | immense 97 | deluge 98 | sinister 100 | toboggans 100 |
| melancholy 101 | horizon 101 | smithereens 103 | interrupted 103 | population 103 |
| subway 103 | plummeted 106 | stupor 106 | plummeted 106 | stupor 106 |

**Directions:** Complete each statement with a word from the box, above.

1. Jackie had predicted that the puppet show would be boring, but now he sat completely __ __ __ __ __ __ __ __ __ __ by it.
   <br>10 16     4

2. After the snowfall, the hill was dotted with sleds and __ __ __ __ __ __ __ __ __.
   <br>5 11   3   9

3. The pelican circled slowly over the sea, then __ __ __ __ __ __ __ __ __ to the surface and snapped up a fish.
   <br>12

4. When the alarm went off, she groggily shut it off and stumbled to the bathroom in a __ __ __ __ __ __.
   <br>7

5. The wicked witch glared __ __ __ __ __ __ __ __ __ __ __ at Hansel and Gretel.
   <br>13    2

6. When the dynamite went off, the shack was blown to __ __ __ __ __ __ __ __ __ __.
   <br>14

7. There is something __ __ __ __ __ __ __ __ about that deserted house with the broken windows.
   <br>15

8.  The babysitter was __ __ __ __ __ __ __ __ __ __ __ __ when the baby-
    $\phantom{xxxxxxxxxxxxxx}$ 1
    boomer parents handed her $4 for eight hours of work.

9.  The weather forecaster predicted a light shower, but there was a
    __ __ __ __ __ __ instead.
    6

10. In Washington, D.C., the underground train is called the metro and in New York
    City it is called the __ __ __ __ __ __.
    $\phantom{xxxxxxxxx}$ 8

**Notice the numbers under some of the letters you have written. Place the correct letter with its matching number on each line below to complete the thought:**

The passenger plane settled the problem posed by the Earthworm:
"How on earth are we going

__ __ __ __ __ __ __ __ __ __ __ __ __ __ __ __ ?"
1  2   3  4  5   6  7  8  9   10 11   12 13 14 15 16

Name_____

| | | | |
|---|---|---|---|
| tapered 107 | pinnacle 107 | Gorgon 109 | cockatrice 110 |
| gaped 111 | chaperone 112 | boon 112 | publicity 113 |
| steeplejacks 115 | ticker-tape 115 | | |

**Directions:** After reading Chapters 36-39 (and reading each of the list words in the context of the story), discuss each of the words in the Vocabulary Box above, and develop a definition or idea of what you think each word means. Then use your context definitions to match the words with the definitions given in Step 2.

**Step 2:**
Find the word that matches each phrase:

1. _____ the highest point; from Latin for "battlement"

2. _____ any of three mythological sisters who had snakes for hair; from Greek for "fearful"

3. _____ He or she builds or repairs towers; from Old English word for tower, "stepel."

4. _____ a benefit or blessing; from Scandinavian word for prayer, "bon"

5. _____ confetti showered along a parade route; literally, the tape on which stock prices and market reports are printed on a telegraphic receiving instrument

6. _____ becoming gradually narrower or smaller

7. _____ a mythical serpent that could kill with a glance

8. _____ an older person who supervises younger people

9. _____ stared, mouth open, filled with wonder

10. _____ information distributed to attract public notice

Name_____

# Attribute Web

| What He Does |
|---|

1. _____
2. _____
3. _____
4. _____

| What He Feels and Thinks |
|---|

1. _____
2. _____
3. _____
4. _____

**James**

| The Life He Left Behind |
|---|

1. _____
2. _____
3. _____
4. _____

| How the Bugs Treat Him |
|---|

1. _____
2. _____
3. _____
4. _____

Name_____

**Directions:** James and the other travelers take a journey in the peach. Map the trip by drawing a picture of each location and writing a caption that summarizes what happens there.

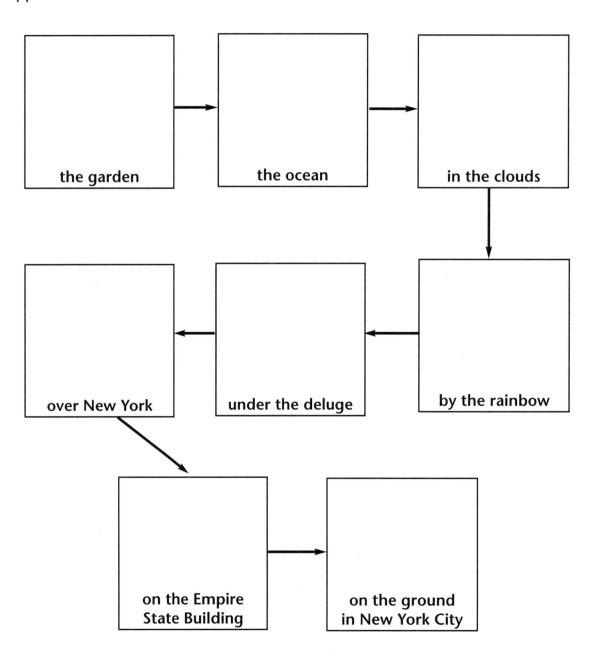

the garden

the ocean

in the clouds

over New York

under the deluge

by the rainbow

on the Empire State Building

on the ground in New York City

Name_____

**Directions:** Add to what you learn from the novel about each of the crawly creatures below by using two or three reference books.

| Creature | Appearance | Foods | Behavior | Home |
|---|---|---|---|---|
| grasshopper | | | | |
| ladybug | | | | |
| silkworm | | | | |
| glow-worm | | | | |
| centipede | | | | |
| spider | | | | |
| earthworm | | | | |

**Directions:** Each character is surrounded by traits (words that describe him or her). Fill in each rectangle with a detail from the story that demonstrates the trait in the circle.

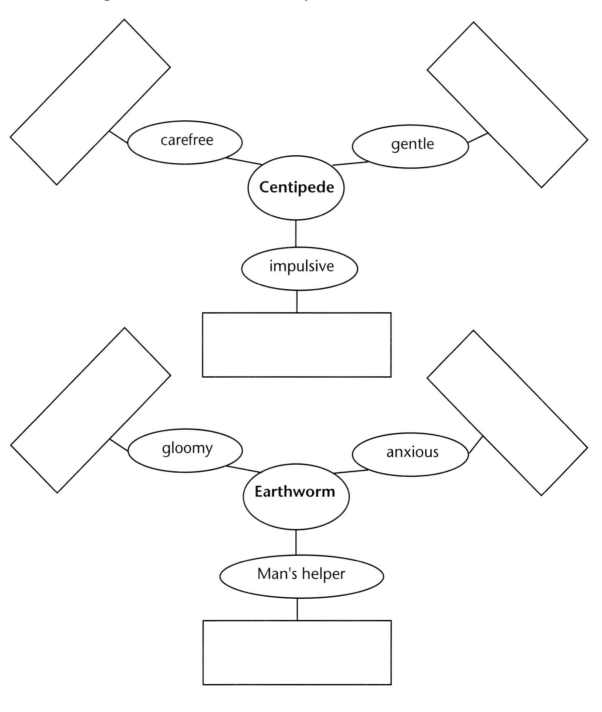

Name_____

**Directions:** Use the finger puppet outlines below to draw characters from *James and the Giant Peach,* and use them and those created by others in your group to act out your favorite part of the story for your class.

**Step 1:** Sketch your two characters on the outlines.
**Step 2:** Glue to cardboard or half of a manila folder. Color and cut out.
**Step 3:** Fold and insert your index and middle fingers, which serve as "legs."
**Step 4:** Rehearse with your group, and then act out your scene on a table or desk.

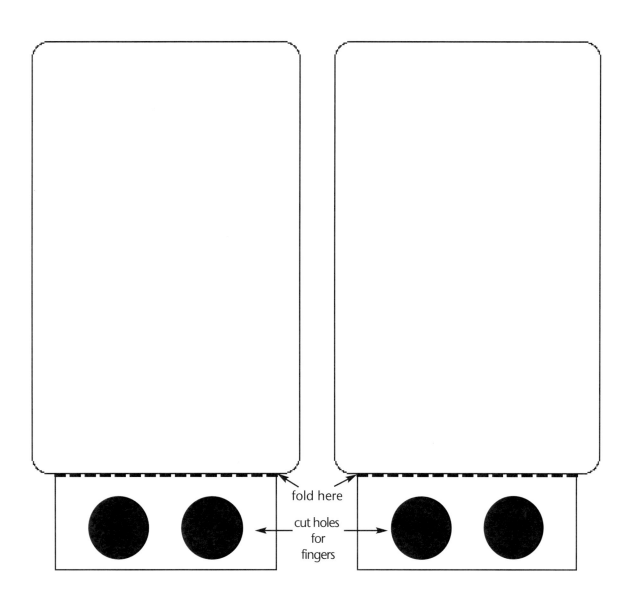

fold here

cut holes
for
fingers

Name_____

*James and the Giant Peach*
Activity #16: **Literary Analysis**
Use After Reading
**Note:** This activity has two pages.
*(Literary Devices)*

**Directions:** Authors sometimes use words in a certain way to make descriptions more vivid for readers. One type of their special language is the **simile.** Similes are comparisons using the words "like" or "as." <u>For</u> <u>example:</u> *Her fingers were like icicles.*

Below are several examples of similes used by Roald Dahl in *James and the Giant Peach.*
  a) Tell what two things are being compared, and how they are alike.
  b) Write your own simile to compare the first thing with the second.

  1. James spent hours gazing at the "forbidden world of woods and fields and ocean that was spread out below him like a magic carpet." (p. 3)

   a) _____ is like _____ because both

   _____.

   b) ...spread out below him like _____

   _____


  2. Aunt Spiker and Aunt Sponge were "like a couple of hunters who had just shot an elephant and were not quite sure whether it was dead or alive." (p. 19)

   a) _____ is like _____ because both

   _____.

   b) Aunt Spiker and Aunt Sponge were like_____

   _____

   _____

3. The aunts "lay ironed out flat upon the grass as flat and thin and lifeless as a couple of paper dolls..." (p. 40)

   a) _____ is like _____ because both

   _____.

   b) ...lifeless as_____

   _____

4. "Everything and all of them were being rattled around like peas inside an enormous rattle that was being rattled by a mad giant who refused to stop." (p. 44)

   a) _____ is like _____ because both

   _____.

   b) ...rattled around like _____

   _____

5. "The hailstones came whizzing through the air like bullets from a machine gun..." (p. 87)

   a) _____ is like _____ because both

   _____.

   b) ....whizzing through the air like _____

   _____

Name_____

*James and the Giant Peach*
Activity #17: **Review Crossword**
**Note:** Clues are on next page.
*(Main Idea and Details)*

**Directions:** Use the clues on the next page to figure out the answers to the crossword.

Name_____

# Crossword Clues

## ACROSS

2. The Old Green-Grasshopper became a member of the New York Symphony_____.
4. James and his aunts lived here.
8. The peach was eaten by these.
10. The Glow-worm got a job at the Statue of____.
11. The Ladybug's greatest fear.
12. Spider and Silkworm made these in their factory.
14. James figured out a plan to get their help.
18. These were called in to get the peach down from the spire.
19. When the green things went into the soil, a big one of these appeared on the tree.
20. This gloomy creature was blind.
22. The peach finally landed in ____ _____.
25. The peach got stuck on the top of the _____ State Building.
27. This creature asked James for help removing its shoes.
28. James found a door in the peach made in the _____.
29. This aunt decided the peach should not be eaten.

## DOWN

1. The green things in the sack were tongues from this animal.
3. The Cloud-Men practiced hurling these.
5. She married the head of the Fire Department.
6. The Earthworm got a job making commercials for _____ cream.
7. The peach was attacked by these.
9. The _____ Men grew angry at the travelers.
13. This creature entertained the others with music.
14. This quiet creature slept most of the time.
15. The crew of this ship thought the captain had been at the whiskey again when he reported the creatures in the peach.
16. This aunt was fat and pulpy.
17. The Centipede became Vice-President of a firm that manufactures these.
21. The Cloud-Men were painting this arch.
23. She made beds for the others.
24. The Centipede's paint problem was solved when the peach passed under a _____.
26. James' parents were eaten by a _____.

Name_____

*(Main Idea and Details)*

**Directions:**  Label each statement "T" for True or "F" for False.  Change the false statements into true ones by changing some of the words or rewriting the statement.

____   1.   James was orphaned when his parents were run over by a tram.

____   2.   James was sent to live with his two nasty aunts, Sponge and Spiker.

____   3.   James was lonely because his aunts never allowed him to play with other children.

____   4.   The old man offered James a bag of green things in exchange for the wood James had chopped.

____   5.   James added water and hair to the green things, as the old man had directed.

____   6.   James' aunts were surprised to see a peach growing on a tree that never gave any peaches.

____   7.   James' aunts decided to hold a public auction and sell the peach.

____   8.   James decided to dig a hole in the peach and see what was inside.

____   9.   The creatures inside the peach had been small before they ate some of the green things.

____   10.   The insects were shocked and frightened at first by James' appearance.

____   11.   The Grasshopper made leaf beds for the others.

____   12.   The Centipede sets the peach loose by nibbling at the stem.

____   13.   The peach rolled over the aunts and down into the ocean.

____   14.   When the creatures got hungry, they ate the sandwiches that James had brought along.

____   15.   Sharks attack the peach.

*(Main Idea and Details)*
**Directions:** Answer each question in one complete sentence.

1. How did James become an orphan?

2. With whom was James sent to live after losing his parents?

3. Why was James lonely and unhappy in his new home?

4. What did the old man offer James?

5. What did the old man tell James to do?

6. Why were James' aunts surprised by the peach tree?

7. How did James' aunts decide to make money from the peach?

8. How did James get inside the peach?

9. How were the creatures inside the peach different from usual and how did they get that way?

10. How did the creatures act toward James?

11. Who made beds for the creatures?

12. How did the peach get loose from the tree?

13. What happened to the aunts?

14. What did the creatures eat when they got hungry?

15. What attacked the peach in the ocean?

Name_____

*(Character Analysis)*

**Identification:** Find a character on the right who matches the description on the left. Write the letter of the character next to the matching number. Each character is to be used only once.

| | | |
|---|---|---|
| __ 1. | She was enormously fat and very short with piggy eyes. | a. James Henry Trotter |
| __ 2. | She was lean and tall and bony with a screeching voice. | b. Aunt Spiker |
| | | c. Aunt Sponge |
| __ 3. | He had a crazy dark green suit and a huge bald head. | d. Old-Green-Grasshopper |
| __ 4. | His parents were eaten by an angry rhinoceros. | e. the Ladybug |
| __ 5. | He proudly calls himself a "pest." | f. the Silkworm |
| __ 6. | She hangs from the ceiling like a light bulb. | g. the Earthworm |
| __ 7. | He acts as a lure for the seagulls. | h. Miss Spider |
| __ 8. | She saw her father flushed down the plughole by Aunt Sponge. | i. the Glow-worm |
| __ 9. | He plays tunes for the others. | j. the Centipede |
| __10. | She marries the head of the Fire Department. | k. the old man |
| __11. | She helps Spider spin thread to catch the seagulls. | |

*(Main Idea and Details)*

**Fill-Ins:** Fill in each blank with the correct word or phrase.

James Henry Trotter became an orphan when his parents were eaten by an escaped 1._____. He was sent to live with his mean 2._____ and grew very lonely. One day he began crying and begged the two women to take him to the 3._____. When they told him to get out of their sight, he ran to the yard where he met an old man who gave him a white 4._____. Inside were 5._____ things that the old man said would change his life. He told James to add 6._____ and 7._____ and swallow. Before James could do so, he tripped and the green things sank into the 8._____ near the 9._____ tree. Soon afterward his aunts discovered a giant 10._____ on the tree, which had always been bare. They decided to make money by charging people to 11.____ it. James was locked up until nightfall, when they sent him out to 12._____ up.  Alone with the peach, he discovered a

13._____ and climbed inside.  Inside he met several insects and other animals, all

as 14.____ as he was.  Each had eaten one or more of the 15._____ things that fell from

the bag and now the magic was at work on them.  The next day, Centipede chewed

through the stem and the peach fell off the tree, rolling over the two 16._____ and

down to the 17.___.  Soon they realized that they would have to get out of the water

or be eaten by 18._____.  Using Earthworm as bait for 19._____, they lassoed the

birds with threads and were carried up into the clouds.  There they saw 20._____

hurling 21._____ and painting 22._____.  A 23._____ passing by cut

all the threads and they fell to earth, landing on the spire of the 24._____

_____ _____in 25.____ _____ City.  A big 26._____ was held in their honor

and the peach was eaten by hundreds of 27._____.  The creatures got good

jobs and James settled down to a happy life in his house,  made out of the

28._____.

## Written Response

**Directions:**  Choose A or B and circle the letter of the question you decide to answer.
*(Conflict/Resolution)*
  **A.** James helped solve several problems.  Choose what you think is the biggest one
      and describe the steps he took in solving it.
*(Summarize Major Ideas)*
  **B.** The old man promised James that after the magic green things went to work,
      James would never be miserable again.  Explain how the magic in the bag ended
      up making James happy.

**Directions:**  Choose C or D and circle the letter of the question you decide to answer.
*(Drawing Conclusions)*
  **C.** Imagine that James had followed the directions the old man gave him.  Describe
      what you think would have happened.
*(Point of View)*
  **D.** Imagine that you are James.  Describe how you felt when the peach rolled over
      your aunts.

Name_____

*(Character Analysis)*

**Identification:** Find a character on the right who matches the quote on the left. Write the letter of the character next to the matching number. Each character is to be used only once.

__ 1. "What a heavenly taste! Up until this moment, I have never in my life tasted anything except those tiny little green flies that live on rosebushes..."

__ 2. (when told to put out the light) "There is no need to be rude. All in good time."

__ 3. "Couldn't we all—please—just for once—go down to the seaside on the bus?"

__ 4. "They [the Cloud-Men] have broken my bulb!"

__ 5. "Crocodile tongues! One thousand long slimy crocodile tongues boiled up in the skull of a dead witch..."

__ 6. "My dear boy. I am a real violin!"

__ 7. "Behold my gorgeous curvy shape, my teeth, my charming grin!"

__ 8. "I am not going to be pecked to death by a bunch of seagulls!"

__ 9. "I think you'd make...a lovely Frankenstein."

__10. "Oh hooray for the storm and the rain!/I can move! I don't feel any pain!"

__11. (She never says anything, and spends most of her time asleep.)

a. James Henry Trotter
b. Aunt Spiker
c. Aunt Sponge
d. Old-Green-Grasshopper
e. the Ladybug
f. the Silkworm
g. the Earthworm
h. Miss Spider
i. the Glow-worm
j. the Centipede
k. the old man

**Multiple Choice:** To the left of each item number, write the number of the BEST response.

*(Character Analysis)*

____ 1. Which of the following words describes the aunts LEAST well?
(1) lazy
(2) greedy
(3) abusive
(4) feeble-minded

*(Cause/Effect)*

_____ 2. What is the most likely reason the aunts took James in?
  (1) They were paid to care for him.
  (2) They planned to have him work for them.
  (3) They felt obliged to take care of family.
  (4) They planned to eat him.

*(Main Idea and Details)*

_____ 3. What did the old man promise James?
  (1) an end to his misery
  (2) wealth
  (3) the death of James' aunts
  (4) friends

*(Cause/Effect)*

_____ 4. If James hadn't tripped and spilled the green things,
  (1) he wouldn't have been orphaned
  (2) the peach wouldn't have grown
  (3) the old man wouldn't have appeared
  (4) the old man wouldn't have disappeared

*(Character Analysis)*

_____ 5. Which of the following creatures would be most likely to look at a cup that is half full and say, "But it's half empty!"
  (1) Glow-worm
  (2) Grasshopper
  (3) Centipede
  (4) Earthworm

*(Character Analysis)*

_____ 6. When James' aunts were flattened, he probably felt mostly
  (1) disgusted
  (2) frightened
  (3) sad
  (4) glad

*(Cause/Effect)*

_____ 7. The Spider was especially happy to get rid of Aunt Sponge and Aunt Spiker because they had
  (1) killed her grandmother and father
  (2) killed her sister and cousin
  (3) flushed her egg sack down the toilet
  (4) destroyed her home with a broom

*(Main Idea and Details)*

___ 8.  Stranded in the peach, the animals ate
(1) sandwiches
(2) bugs
(3) the peach
(4) seagulls

*(Cause/Effect)*

___ 9.  It was necessary to get the peach out of the ocean because
(1) it salt water was eating away at the peach
(2) the peach sprung a leak
(3) sharks attacked
(4) seagulls were pecking at the peach

*(Main Idea and Details)*

___ 10.  James got the seagulls to lift the peach by
(1) promising them bites of the peach
(2) tossing lassoes around their necks
(3) promising to return the favor some day
(4) throwing things at them

*(Main Idea and Details)*

___ 11.  When the Cloud-Men first came in sight, they were
(1) preparing hailstones to hurl down on the earth
(2) playing thundering nine-pins
(3) painting a rainbow
(4) stirring up a cyclone

*(Main Idea and Details)*

___ 12.  The Cloud-Men poured paint
(1) accidentally over the rainbow
(2) angrily over the Centipede
(3) laughingly over the Peach
(4) deliberately over the countryside

*(Main Idea and Details)*

___ 13.  According to this story, the rainbow gets its color from
(1) the oil from the Cloud-Women's frying pans
(2) the sea's reflection
(3) the Cloud-Men's paint
(4) the flowers that seagulls drop in the air

*(Main Idea and Details)*

____ 14.　The giant peach landed on
(1) the tower of London, in London, England
(2) the John Hancock Building, in Hartford
(3) the Pyramid, in San Francisco
(4) the Empire State Building, in New York

*(Author's Purpose)*

____ 15.　James wrote the story of *James and the Giant Peach*
(1) for the children of his insect friends who would never otherwise have heard it
(2) for the children who came from far and near to hear of his adventures
(3) to earn money for supporting himself in his new home
(4) in a diary which he kept quietly under his pillow without ever sharing it with anyone

## Written Response

I.　**Analysis:** Select A or B and circle the letter of the question you decide to answer.

*(Character Analysis)*

**A.** Select your favorite creature in the story and describe what it is like. Explain why that personality is fitting for such a creature.

*(Compare/Contrast)*

**B.** Compare and contrast one of the aunts with a figure from a fairy tale, such as Snow White's wicked stepmother.

II.　**Critical and Creative Thinking:** Select C or D and circle the letter of the question you decide to answer.

*(Write to Express)*

**C.** This book contains some violence. Describe at least two examples and explain why you do or do not feel that such violence belongs in a book for children.

*(Point of View/Write to Entertain)*

**D.** Pretend that you are the Centipede. Write a short rhyme for James as a "housewarming" present when he moves into his new house in New York.

# Answer Key

## Study Questions

### Chapters 1-6

1. They are eaten by a rhinoceros. 2. He moves in with his mean aunts and grows lonely. 3. in a dilapidated house on a hill in southern England 4. Aunt Sponge is fat and "spongy" and Aunt Spiker is thin and angular (spikey). 5. The sisters quarrel; Aunt Sponge proclaims her own beauty while Aunt Spiker reminds her how fat she is. 6. Both abuse him by calling him names, making him constantly do chores. 7. He is never allowed to play with other children. 8. a bag with magic green things inside, supposedly capable of removing his misery 9. He is supposed to add water and hairs and drink, but he drops the bag near the peach tree and the green things spill out. 10. The aunts are watching the peach grow after the green things crept into the soil beneath it.

### Chapters 7-12

11. Aunt Sponge wants to eat it, but Aunt Spiker wants to wait and make money out of it. 12. to save it from the crowd of onlookers 13. one shilling (about 14 cents). 14. jumpy and scared 15. As he looks at the peach, he has a premonition that something strange is about to happen soon. 16. He creeps into a tunnel he discovers, finds a door cut into the face of the pit, and pushes his way in. 17. They have been waiting for James and seem to know all about him and his aunts. 18. He is frightened, but he soon relaxes after they assure him that they do not want to eat him and that he is one of them. 19. The centipede is considered a pest by farmers and gardeners because it eats crops. 20. The Centipede laughs, and laughter is something James hasn't heard in a long time.

### Chapters 13-17

21. Miss Spider spins beds for the others; the Glow-worm provides light. 22. She has a lot of shoes to remove; untangling laces can be frustrating for children, but James helps respectfully. 23. They seem to know that James has been miserable here and would enjoy a change; the Centipede bites through the stem. 24. the Centipede 25. His rhyme (pp. 37-38) shows that he relishes the idea of all sorts of adventures and misadventures. 26. They get flattened by the rolling peach. 27. It rolls down the hill— flattening cars, frightening animals; the "ands" convey a sense of the speed and unstoppability of the rolling peach because the reader doesn't pause, as he would for commas or periods. 28. the white cliffs of Dover 29. in the sea 30. Miss Spider weaves a rope ladder.

### Chapters 18-20

31. The Earthworm grumbles about how they will all perish, while the Grasshopper predicts that "Everything will be all right in the end." (p. 48) 32. The Earthworm points out that he literally can't see; he is blind. 33. The Earthworm worries that they will sink into the sea as the peach disappears, but James points out how long it would take to make a dent in such a huge peach. 34. This is a song of praise to the peach for its glorious taste. 35. Sharks attack the peach. 36. He will lasso seagulls, using threads spun by the Silkworm and Spider, with the Earthworm as bait. 37. They all think James' plan for lassoing seagulls is absurd. 38. The Centipede thinks that James' rescue plan shows that he is "crazy." 39. The seagulls will eat the Earthworm. 40. Answers will vary; he outlines the details of his plan to have the Earthworm lie half out of the peach while he readies the lasso for the swooping seagulls.

### Chapters 21-24

41. Frightened; he probably feels that this is the only chance they all have. 42. He throws a loop of silk around each bird's neck. 43. Enough gulls have been lassoed to raise the peach from the water, and the passengers have climbed out to take a look around. 44.Spider descends to take a look at the damage caused by the sharks. 45. The shape of the shark's jaw makes it hard to fit around a curved peach. 46. out of the English Channel to America. 47. All are mistrustful of the "flying ball's" motives; when the Captain reports sighting a boy and creatures on the peach, the others think he has been drinking. 48. The Grasshopper plays music. 49. Short-horned and long-horned varieties make music in different ways.

50. When James mentions finding it odd that the Grasshopper's ears are on its tummy, the Grasshopper counters by saying it is silly to have ears on your head.

*Chapters 25-27*

51. Earthworms loosen and aerate the soil, making plants grow better. 52. Ladybugs eat pests. 53. Aunt Sponge had flushed her father. 54. the demise of the two aunts 55. It has the same meter and rhyme scheme (5 lines, aabba) 56. He gets so carried away with his singing and dancing that he falls overboard. 57. James has the Silkworm spin a life rope and goes after the Centipede. 58. the Funeral March; He thought the Centipede was a goner. 59. Cloud-Men rolling hailstones; they are chanting delightedly about giving people colds. 60. He taunts them and they start throwing hailstones at the peach.

*Chapters 28-34*

61. a rainbow 62. He'd rather be fish-bait than have to encounter the terrifying Cloud-Men again. 63. The peach's threads get caught up in the rainbow. 64. The Centipede bites off that string and a seagull flies away with the Cloud-Man. 65. They are shocked and drop the rainbow, then throw paint buckets and other objects. 66. One Cloud-Man pours purple paint over him. 67.Her late grandmother was trapped in Aunt Spiker's paint. 68. The Cloud-Men pass overhead and release a cloudburst of rain; the paint is washed off the Centipede. 69. Cloud-Men's wives frying snowballs; factories where cyclones are made  70. He plans to cut loose a few seagulls and drift gently to the ground, but a passing plane severs all the threads.

*Chapters 35-39*

71. The peach's descent is halted by the spire of the Empire State Building. 72. "Ahoy there" is usually a nautical saying. 73. They panic, fleeing for underground shelters (built during the early 1960's in case of nuclear attack); they fear the worst—that the travelers are some sort of malevolent monsters. 74. Manticores and Gorgons and Cockatrices are mythical monsters; the others are made-up names. 75. The usual fireman's term is "hook and ladder." 76. They decide to welcome the travelers once James appears to reassure everyone that the creatures are well-intentioned. 77. He introduces each in rhyme, as the Centipede might. 78. They are helped down—perhaps via ladders and ropes. 79. the mayor 80. Steeplejacks get it down and the children eat it. The Centipede becomes vice-president of a shoe manufacturing firm. The Earthworm advertises women's face cream. The Silkworm and Spider set up a tightrope factory.  The Glow-worm becomes the light in the torch of the Statue of Liberty. The Grasshopper becomes a member of the New York Symphony Orchestra, the Ladybug marries the head of the Fire Department. ("Ladybug, Ladybug, fly away home; your house is on fire; your children are gone"—she had a terrible fear of fire. James lives in the peach stone in the park, where children come to hear him tell of his adventures.

## Activities

Answers to **Activities #1, #2** and other open-ended activities will vary.

**Activity #3:** Word maps will vary.  All words should be mapped.

**Activity #4:** B.1-marvel; 2-famished; 3-seething; 4-intently; 5-scornful; 6-withering; 7-stone; 8-massive, gigantic, mammoth, colossal; 9-bittersweet; 10-bolt

**Activity #5:** 1. chaos-order; paddock-stable  2. repulsive-comely; bleak-desolate  3. disentangled-knotted; lurched-staggered  4.vertically-horizontally; insidiously-treacherously  5. ignore-gape; saunter-amble;  6. elementary-complicated; cobweb-gossamer 7. serenely-tumultuously; hurtling-rushing

**Activity #6:**  Set #1-perambulator; Set #2-grisly; Set #3-pandemonium; Set #4-aghast

**Activity #7:**  1. katydids; 2. tethered; 3. inferior; 4. rambunctious; 5. ascent

**Activity #8:** 1-infuriated; 2-vital; 3-menacing; 4-imbeciles; 5-wraithlike; 6-loathsome; 7-lurking; 8-companions; 9-overwhelming; 10-saucy

Message:  Farmers love us because we help the soil.

**Activity #9:** 1-enthralled; 2-toboggans; 3-plummeted; 4-stupor; 5-malevolently; 6-smithereens; 7-sinister; 8-flabbergasted; 9-deluge; 10-subway.  How on earth are we going ...to get down to earth?

**Activity #10:** 1-pinnacle; 2-Gorgon; 3-steeplejack; 4-boon; 5-ticker-tape; 6-tapered; 7-cockatrice; 8-chaperone; 9-gaped; 10-publicity

**Activity #11:** Attribute Webs will vary; James is about seven, feels lonely living with his aunts; works hard; is a good problem-solver

**Activity #12:** Maps will vary.

**Activity #13:** Charts will vary.

**Activity #14:** Sample answers: Centipede-carefree (likes to sing and dance); gentle (according to James' introduction); impulsive (taunts Cloud-Men without thinking); Earthworm-gloomy (predicts that they will drown); man's helper (describes how earthworms aerate the farmer's soil; anxious (worries about being eaten by seagulls)

**Activities #15:** no specific answers

**Activity #16:** 1-a The world is like a magic carpet to him; both are spread out, full of tantalizing promise; 2-a The aunts are like elephant hunters; they aren't sure whether it is safe yet to get close to their "prey"—the peach; 3-a The aunts are like paper dolls; both are flat and lifeless; 4-a The contents of the rolling peach are like the contents of a giant's rattle; both are shaken hard over and over and bang around inside;5-a The hailstones are like bullets; both travel very fast, with great destructive power

**Activity #17:**

**Comprehension Quiz** (Correcting True-False)

1-F (when they were eaten by a rhino); 2-T; 3-T; 4-F (The man offered the green things for nothing.); 5-F (Before James could follow the directions, he tripped and lost the green things.); 6-T; 7-F (They decided to charge people admission to see the peach.); 8-F (He found a tunnel and followed it.); 9-T; 10-F (James was horrified by the creatures at first, but they greeted him calmly.); 11-F (The spider spun webs for the others.) 12-T; 13-T; 14-F (They ate the peach.); 15-T

**Comprehension Quiz** (Short Answer)

1-An angry rhino escaped from the zoo and ate James' parents. 2-with his Aunt Sponge and Aunt Spiker; 3-His aunts abused him and wouldn't let him play with other children. 4-a white sack full of green things; 5-add water and hair to the green things and drink them; He would no longer be miserable. 6-They had never seen any peaches grow on it before and now a huge peach kept growing and growing. 7-by charging people a shilling to see it; 8-He followed a tunnel he found, then pushed through the stone-pit door at the center. 9-They were as large as James and talked; they had swallowed the magical green things. 10-friendly, as if they expected him; 11-the Spider; 12-The Centipede chewed the stem from the tree. 13-They were flattened by the rolling peach. 14-the peach; 15-sharks

**Novel Test**

Identification: 1-c; 2-b; 3-k; 4-a; 5-j; 6-i; 7-g; 8-h; 9-d; 10-e; 11-f

Fill-Ins: 1-rhino; 2-aunts; 3-seaside; 4-bag; 5-green; 6-water; 7-hairs; 8-soil; 9-peach; 10-peach; 11-see; 12-clean; 13-tunnel; 14-large; 15-green; 16-aunts; 17-ocean; 18-sharks; 19-seagulls; 20-Cloud-Men; 21-hailstones; 22-rainbows; 23-plane; 24-Empire State Building; 25-New York; 26-parade; 27-children; 28-stone (peach pit).

Written Response (sample answers)

A. Students might describe the steps James took in getting the peach out of the ocean: explaining his plan, getting the thread spun, convincing the Earthworm to act as bait, lassoing the seagulls. B. Students who choose B should mention that the magic led James to the creatures, who got him away from his mean aunts, and involved him in an adventure which ended with his telling stories to hundreds of children—and ending his loneliness.

Students who choose **C** might predict that James would have become an invincible giant. Students who choose **D** might support the idea that James felt satisfied and relieved to see the demise of his nasty aunts.

**Novel Test** (Advanced Level)

Identification: 1-e; 2-h; 3-a; 4-i; 5-k; 6-d; 7-c; 8-g; 9-b; 10-j; 11-f

Multiple Choice: 1-4; 2-2; 3-1; 4-2; 5-4; 6-4; 7-1; 8-3; 9-3; 10-2; 11-1; 12-2; 13-3; 14-4; 15-2

Written Response: (sample answers)

Students who select **A** might, for example, defend the idea that the Earthworm's anxious personality is fitting, since he does have to worry about being eaten by birds, and about threats to which he is blind. B. Students who select **B** might, for example, point out that Aunt Sponge, like Snow White's wicked stepmother, is taken with her own "beauty"—feels no remorse about abusing an innocent child, and ultimately gets her "just desserts." Students who select **C** might point to the violent deaths of James' parents, his aunts, the Spider's relatives—but support the idea that this story, like Grimm's fairy tales, helps children work through some of their fears while providing an entertaining story. **D.** Rhymes will vary, and might include memories of times they shared together in the peach, thanks for James' part in getting the Centipede out of various scrapes, and wishes for happiness in his peach-pit home.

# Linking Novel Units® Student Packets to National and State Reading Assessments

During the past several years, an increasing number of students have faced some form of state-mandated competency testing in reading. Many states now administer state-developed assessments to measure the skills and knowledge emphasized in their particular reading curriculum. This Novel Units® guide includes open-ended comprehension questions that correlate with state-mandated reading assessments. The rubric below provides important information for evaluating responses to open-ended comprehension questions. Teachers may also use scoring rubrics provided for their own state's competency test.

## Scoring Rubric for Open-Ended Items

**3-Exemplary**
Thorough, complete ideas/information
Clear organization throughout
Logical reasoning/conclusions
Thorough understanding of reading task
Accurate, complete response

**2-Sufficient**
Many relevant ideas/pieces of information
Clear organization throughout most of response
Minor problems in logical reasoning/conclusions
General understanding of reading task
Generally accurate and complete response

**1-Partially Sufficient**
Minimally relevant ideas/information
Obvious gaps in organization
Obvious problems in logical reasoning/conclusions
Minimal understanding of reading task
Inaccuracies/incomplete response

**0-Insufficient**
Irrelevant ideas/information
No coherent organization
Major problems in logical reasoning/conclusions
Little or no understanding of reading task
Generally inaccurate/incomplete response